LITTLE BIG BOOK
PLUS

Table of Contents

Meet Patricia Lillie

Patricia Lillie works at the Henderson Memorial Public Library in Jefferson, Ohio. All year long she collects and shares children's books.

Meet Donald Crews

Donald Crews took black-and-white photographs for this book. Then he added color. He says that taking pictures of the objects made him feel like a collector.

When This Box Is Full

By
Patricia Lillie

Pictures by
Donald Crews

HOUGHTON MIFFLIN COMPANY
BOSTON
ATLANTA   DALLAS   GENEVA, ILLINOIS   PALO ALTO   PRINCETON

Acknowledgments

For each of the selections listed below, grateful acknowledgment is made for permission to excerpt and/or reprint original or copyrighted material, as follows:

Text

1 *When This Box Is Full,* by Patricia Lillie. Illustrated by Donald Crews. Text copyright © 1993 by Patricia Lillie. Illustrations copyright © 1993 by Donald Crews. Reprinted by permission of Greenwillow Books, a division of William Morrow & Company. **24** "The Four Seasons," from September 1994 Series II *Your Big Backyard* magazine. Copyright © 1981 by the National Wildlife Federation. Reprinted by permission. **26** "Almanac for the New Year," from *Skip Around the Year,* by Aileen Fisher. Copyright © 1967 by Aileen Fisher. Reprinted by permission of HarperCollins Publishers.

Illustrations

24–25 Racquel Sousa. **26** Racquel Sousa.

Photography

i Tony Scarpetta. **ii** Courtesy of Donald Crews (m). **21** Kindra Clineff (tr, mr, bl). **22** Bob Daemmrich/Stock Boston. **24** C. Gable Ray (cover). **24–25** Walter Chandoha.

Houghton Mifflin Edition, 1997

ISBN 0-395-80433-7

3456789-B-98 97

For Peg and Paula,
for sharing
their chocolate
with me
— P. L.

For Nina and Michael
and everyone
who's ever had
something special
to put in a box
— D. C.

This box is empty... but not for long.

I will fill it with...

January

a snowman's scarf,

January
February
March

**a red
foil heart,**

a robin's feather,

9

January
February
March
April

a purple
eggshell,

January
February
March
April
May
June

a wild
daisy,

**helicopters
from the
maple tree,**

January
February
March
April
May
June
July

a seashell
and some
sand,

January

February

March

April

May

June

July

August

a ribbon
from
the fair,

January
February
March
April
May
June
July
August
September

**a red
leaf,**

January

February

March

April

May

June

July

August

September

October

toasted
pumpkin
seeds,

January
February
March
April
May
June
July
August
September
October
November
December

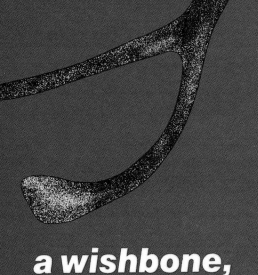

a wishbone,

and
a silver
star.

And then...

23

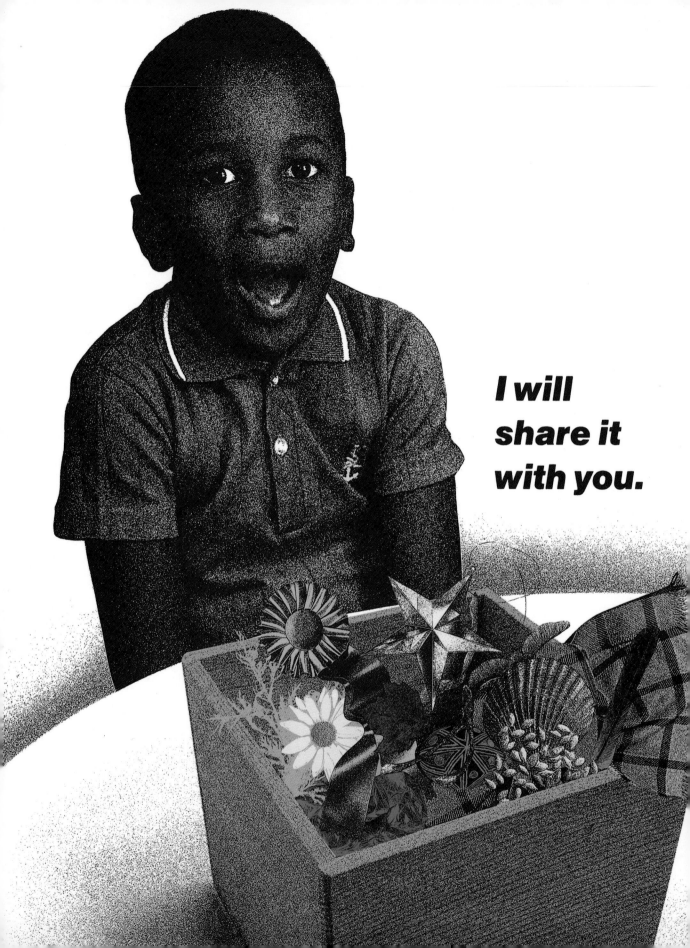

I will
share it
with you.

Jump In!

Sheep in the meadow,
Cows in the corn.
Jump in on the month
    that you were born.
January, February,
    March, April . . .

April is fourth!
Jump four times!

In jumps August!

Here comes July!

25

Great Collections

soapstone

malachite

agate

jasper

granite

talc

turquoise

rose quartz

pyrite

These collectors found their rocks outdoors. You can also buy rocks in special stores.

Here are some
more collections.
What things
do you like
to collect?

The Four Seasons

The leaves are gone
from the trees.
The branches are bare.
What season is it?

The buds open.
New, light green
leaves come out.
What season is it?

Dark green leaves
fill the trees.
They give shade.
What season is it?

The leaves change colors.
Soon they will die and
fall to the ground.
What season is it?

Almanac for the New Year

January – frosted sun.
February – party fun.
March – a windy hint of spring.
April – bluebirds on the wing.
May – a wash of green all over.
June – a pasture full of clover.
For July – a picnic spot.
August – lazy, wilty, hot.
September – haze upon the air.
October – color everywhere.
November – time for thanks again.
December – peace, good will to men.

That's the way the months appear
As we skip around the year.

by Aileen Fisher